Coping Crew

Book #4

A Turtle

Afraid of Enclosed Spaces

Written by: Stacey Lantagne | Illustrated by: Lynne Lillge

Italic Illustrator Shop

A Turtle Afraid of Enclosed Spaces
Coping Crew Book #4

Written by Stacey Lantagne
Illustrated by Lynne Lillge

Distributed in partnership with
Mythic North Press, LLC

https://www.italicillustratorshop.com/
https://www.craftersoncentral.com/

ISBN: 978-1-954177-28-4

Dedication

Readers who have now enjoyed the first several books of the Coping Crew Series have by now seen that every book dedication will always be dedicated to my family.
This includes my husband, three children, mother and grandson, Ezra.
I also dedicate and thank each of my books to my illustrator. Tommy the turtle was a struggle to envision at first but in time she grew to love him and the book. Sometimes she will send me an image and it is spot on with how I envisioned the page to look when I wrote the book.
I'm so thankful for our working partnership and new found friendship.
This book is dedicated to all of those same special people but I would also like to dedicate this to all rescue workers.
There are situations that come up where people or even animals get trapped in various places. These rescue workers work hard to help ensure our safety, prevent these things from happening and help us in our times of need.
Thank you for your service!
In closing, I of course thank each of my readers and hope that you enjoy this fourth book in our series.
Thank you for continuing to inspire me!

You are not alone... You have us.

He didn't want to be scared.
He wished he hadn't cared.

One day while Tommy
was sitting in the sun,
a little boy named David
asked him to have some fun.

Tommy liked this game but now he had fear.

He didn't want David
to leave quite just yet.

David laughed and he cheered.
Tommy did it some more.
In went his head
then he counted to four.

OUT popped his head and David would smile. Tommy realized his shell was not scary all the while.

Hi Readers!

Thank you for purchasing this book. I hope that you have enjoyed it and that you carry it along with you on trips in the car.

Your animal friends in this book would love to join you at school or daycare. They would love to go to the beach or the library.

Perhaps they could even keep you company when you are sick or before bed at night.

My name is Stacey. Can you think of other words that start with the "S" sound?

What kind of animals start with the "S" sound?

I am the author of this book. This means that I came up with the words that either you or someone else read on the pages.

I have always wanted to write a book. I spend a lot of time in libraries with my large English Mastiff dog named Thor. Thor and I do pet therapy with kids and adults of all ages.

Some of our favorite books to hear are ones that rhyme like this book does.

In the past I have had numerous phobias and anxieties in my life.
Sometimes it can be hard to get over a fear.
I have had to learn different techniques and tricks to help me conquer my fears.
It is because of these phobias that I felt inspired to write this book. I want you all to know that you, too, can overcome obstacles and feel proud of yourselves when you achieve them.
Please do not ever feel alone in your fears or afraid to talk to someone about them.
There are so many wonderful tricks to help you.

I grew up a Yooper.
Do you know what that means? It means that I lived in the Upper Peninsula of Michigan (U.P.).
We have four beautiful seasons in the U.P. but our longest season is definitely winter. Do you get snow where you are from?
Can you find the U.P. on a map?

I no longer live in Michigan though. Now I live just across the border in the state of Wisconsin.
My husband and I own an art studio called Crafters on Central.
If you are ever traveling to Wisconsin, we hope that you can stop in to see our studio and get creative with a new art project.
We have a lot of fun things for a variety of ages.
We even have a splatter space that people can get REALLY messy in.
If you liked this book we hope that you get to meet other friends in our Coping Crew series.
Hopefully you can collect them all and that these characters become your friends just like I can be!
Choose to shine in all that you do!

Stacey

Ingram Content Group UK Ltd.
Milton Keynes UK
UKRC030113190423
420242UK00003BA/3